Arranged for all portable keyboards *by Kenr* *ker.*

THE COMPLE
KEYBOARD PLAYER

ABBA

Wise Publications
London/New York/Paris/Sydney/Copenhagen/Madrid

Exclusive Distributors:
Music Sales Limited
14-15 Berners Street, London W1T 3LJ. UK.
Music Sales Pty Limited
20 Resolution Drive, Caringbah, NSW 2229, Australia.

Order No.AM91095
ISBN 0-7119-3426-6
This book © Copyright 1993 by Wise Publications

Book design by Studio Twenty, London
Compiled by Peter Evans
Music arranged by Kenneth Baker
Music processed by Seton Music Graphics

Photographs courtesy of
Pictorial Press

Your Guarantee of Quality
As publishers, we strive to produce every book to the
highest commercial standards.
The music has been freshly engraved and the book has been
carefully designed to minimise awkward page turns and to make
playing from it a real pleasure.
Particular care has been given to specifying acid-free, neutral-sized paper
made from pulps which have not been elemental chlorine bleached.
This pulp is from farmed sustainable forests and was produced with
special regard for the environment.
Throughout, the printing and binding have been planned to ensure a sturdy,
attractive publication which should give years of enjoyment.
If your copy fails to meet our high standards, please inform
us and we will gladly replace it.

I DO, I DO, I DO, I DO, I DO

Words & Music by Benny Andersson, Stig Anderson & Björn Ulvaeus

Suggested registration: flute
Rhythm: swing
Tempo: quite fast (♩ = 132)

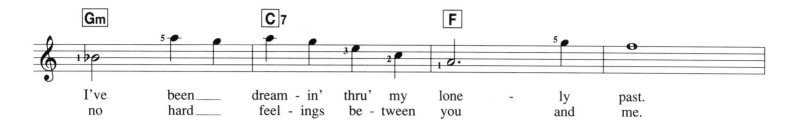

I've been___ dream - in' thru' my lone - ly past.
no hard___ feel - ings be - tween you and me.

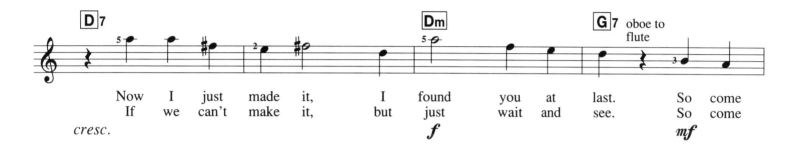

Now I just made it, I found you at last. So come
If we can't make it, but found just you wait and last. see. So come

cresc.

on, now let's try it, I love you, can't de -
on, now let's try it, I love you, can't de -

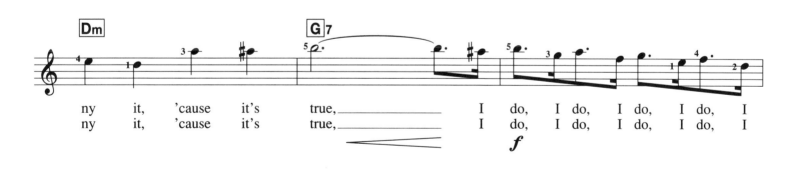

ny it, 'cause it's true,_____ I do, I do, I do, I do, I
ny it, 'cause it's true,_____ I do, I do, I do, I do, I

do.
do.

stop rhythm

FERNANDO
Words & Music by Benny Andersson, Stig Anderson & Björn Ulvaeus

Suggested registration: guitar
Rhythm: rock
Tempo: medium (♩ = 112)

VERSES

Can you hear the drums Fer - nan - do?___ I re - mem - ber long a-
They were clo - ser now, Fer - nan - do.___ Ev - 'ry hour___ ev' - ry

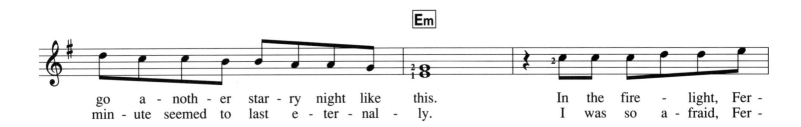

go a - noth - er star - ry night like this. In the fire - light, Fer -
min - ute seemed to last e - ter - nal - ly. I was so a - fraid, Fer -

nan - do,___ You were hum - ming to your - self and soft - ly strum - ming your gui-
nan - do,___ We were young and full of life and none of us pre - pared to

tar. I could hear the dis - tant drums and sounds of bu - gle calls were com - ing from a - far.
die. And I'm not a - shamed to say the roar of guns and can - nons al - most made me cry.

CHORUS

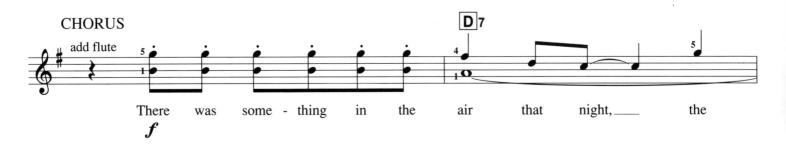

add flute

There was some - thing in the air that night,___ the

f

stars were bright,__ Fer - nan - do.__ They were shin - ing there for

you and me,__ for li - ber - ty,__ Fer - nan - do. Though we

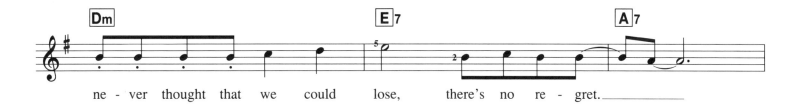

ne - ver thought that we could lose, there's no re - gret.__

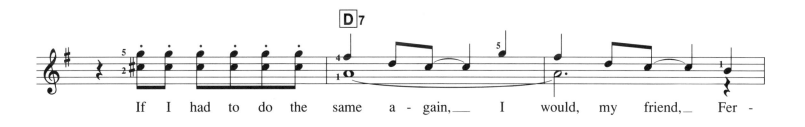

If I had to do the same a - gain,__ I would, my friend,__ Fer -

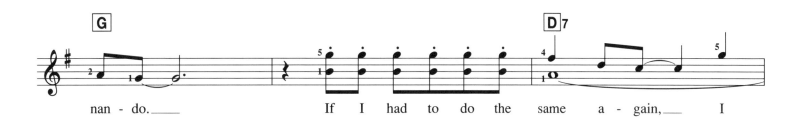

nan - do.__ If I had to do the same a - gain, I

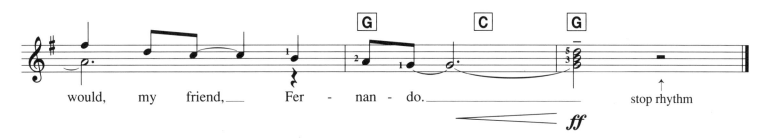

would, my friend,__ Fer - nan - do._____ stop rhythm

_ff_

THE WINNER TAKES IT ALL

Words & Music by Benny Andersson & Björn Ulvaeus

Suggested registration: piano
Rhythm: rock
Tempo: medium (♩ = 104)

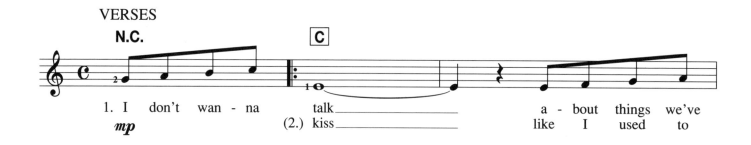

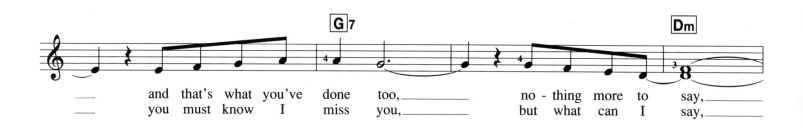

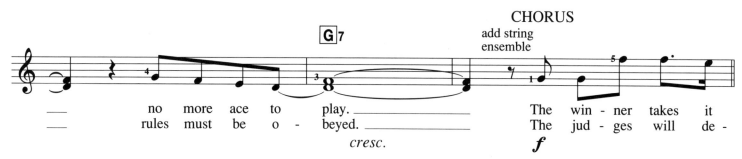

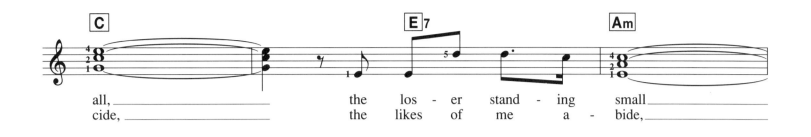

all,_____ the los - er stand - ing small_____
cide,_____ the likes of me a - bide,_____

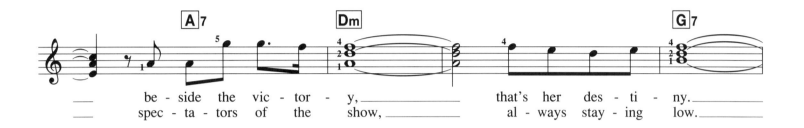

___ be - side the vic - tor - y,_____ that's her des - ti - ny._____
___ spec - ta - tors of the show,_____ al - ways stay - ing low._____

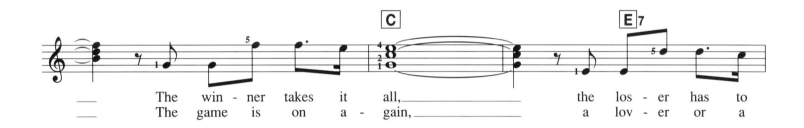

___ The win - ner takes it all,_____ the los - er has to
___ The game is on a - gain,_____ a lov - er or a

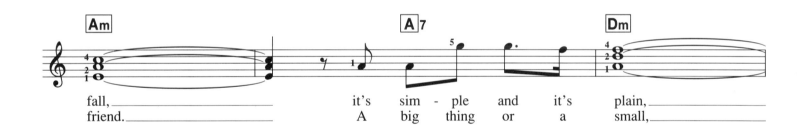

fall,_____ it's sim - ple and it's plain,_____
friend._____ A big thing or a small,_____

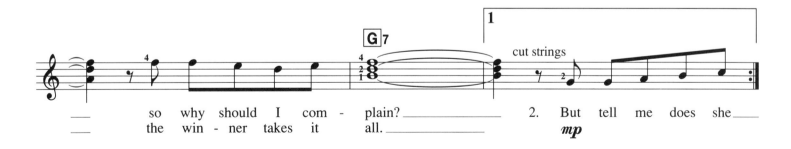

___ so why should I com - plain?_____ 2. But tell me does she_____
___ the win - ner takes it all._____ *mp*

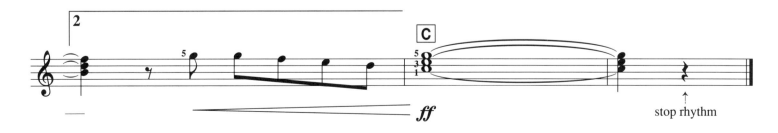

cut strings

ff   stop rhythm

9

THE NAME OF THE GAME

Words & Music by Benny Andersson, Stig Anderson & Björn Ulvaeus

Suggested registration: trumpet
Rhythm: rock
Tempo: fairly fast (melody ♩ = 160)
　　　　　　　　(rhythm ♩ = 80)

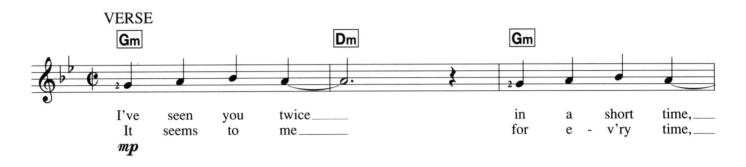

I've seen you twice_____ in a short time,___
It seems to me_____ for e - v'ry time,___

___ on - ly a week_____ since we start -
___ I'm get - ting more_____ o - pen heart -

trumpet to
guitar

___ ed._____ I was an im - pos - si - ble case,
___ ed._____

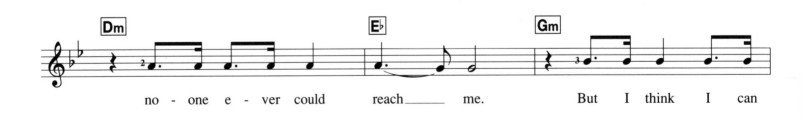

no - one e - ver could reach_____ me. But I think I can

see in your face, there's a lot you can teach_____ me,_____ so I

cresc.

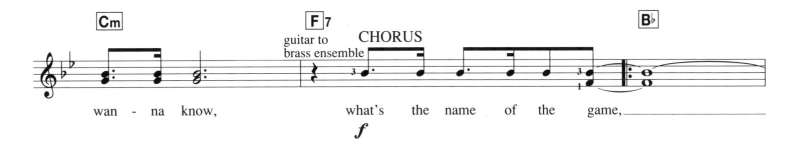

wan - na know,   what's   the   name   of   the   game,_____

_____ does   it   mean   a - ny - thing_____   to   you?_____

What's   the   name   of   the   game,_____

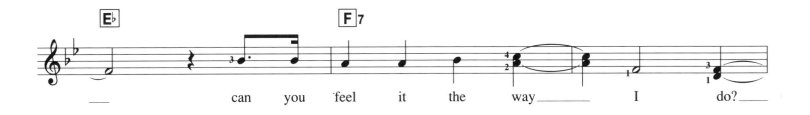

can   you   feel   it   the   way_____   I   do?_____

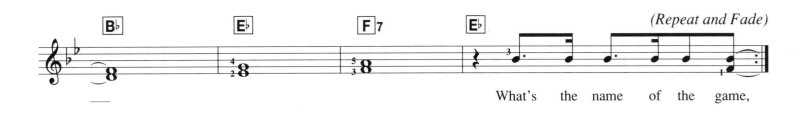

What's   the   name   of   the   game,

11

HASTA MAÑANA

Words & Music by Benny Andersson, Stig Anderson & Björn Ulvaeus

Suggested registration: violin
Rhythm: swing
Tempo: medium 2 (♩ = 88)

VERSES

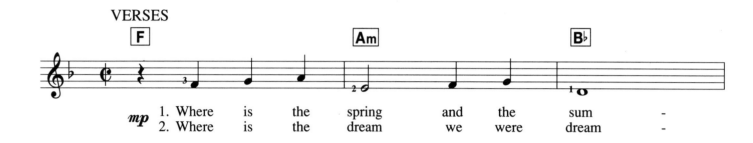

mp
1. Where is the spring and the sum -
2. Where is the dream we were dream -

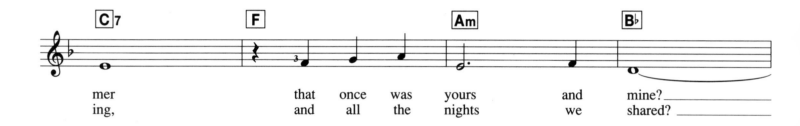

mer that once was yours and mine?
ing, and all the nights we shared?

Where did it go?
Where did they go?

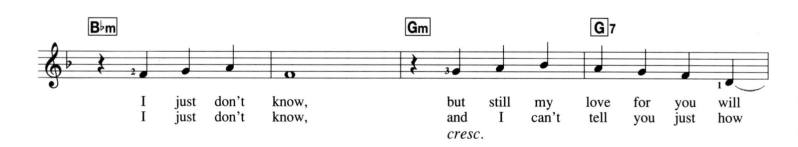

I just don't know, but still my love for you will
I just don't know, and I can't tell you just how
cresc.

CHORUS

violin to flute

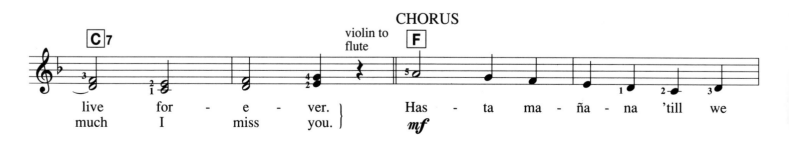

live for - e - ver. Has - ta ma - ña - na 'till we
much I miss you. *mf*

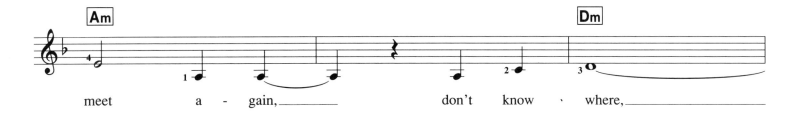

meet a - gain,_____ don't know where,_____

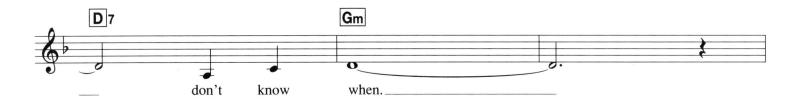

_____ don't know when._____

Dar - ling our love was much too strong to die,_____

we'll find a way to face a

new to - mor - row. Has - ta ma -

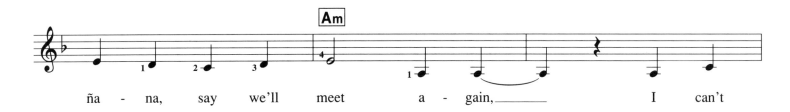

ña - na, say we'll meet a - gain,_____ I can't

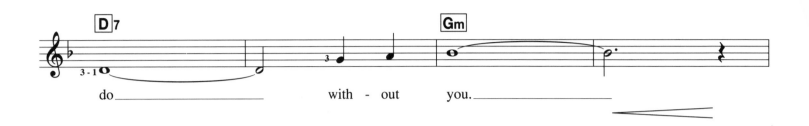

do_____ with - out you._____

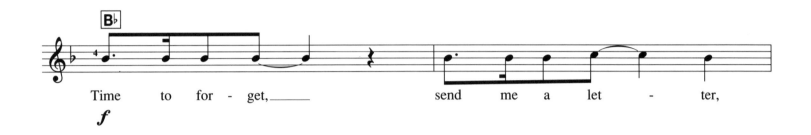

Time to for - get,_____ send me a let - ter,

f

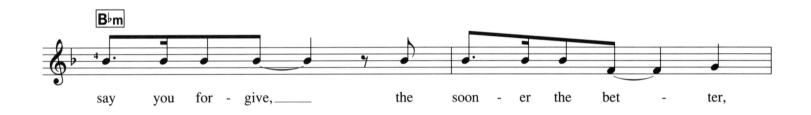

say you for - give,_____ the soon - er the bet - ter,

has - ta ma - ña - na, ba - by, has - ta ma -

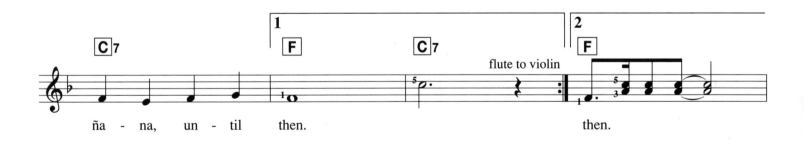

ña - na, un - til then. then.

flute to violin

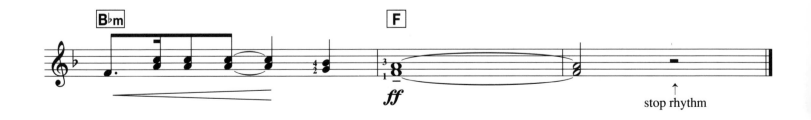

ff

stop rhythm

SUPER TROUPER

Words & Music by Benny Andersson & Björn Ulvaeus

Suggested registration: human voice
Rhythm: rock
Tempo: medium (♩ = 120)

CHORUS

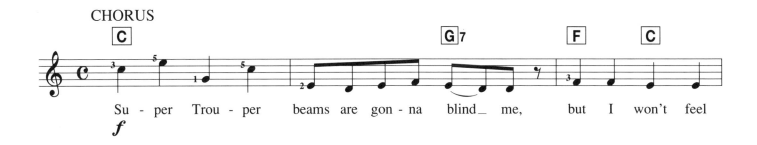

INSTRUMENTAL

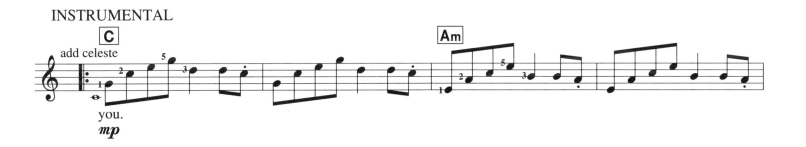

VERSES

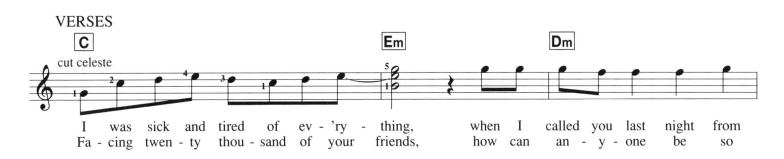

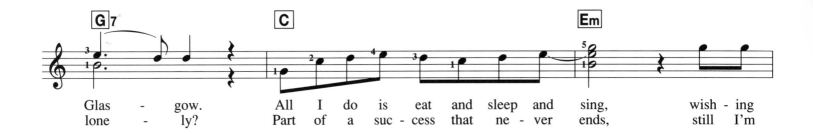

Glas - gow. All I do is eat and sleep and sing, wish - ing
lone - ly? Part of a suc - cess that ne - ver ends, still I'm

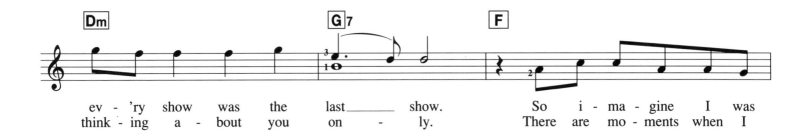

ev - 'ry show was the last_____ show. So i - ma - gine I was
think - ing a - bout you on - ly. There are mo - ments when I

glad to hear you're com - ing, sud - den - ly I feel al - right, and it's gon - na be so
think I'm go - ing cra - zy, but it's gon - na be al - right. Ev - 'ry thing will be so
cresc.

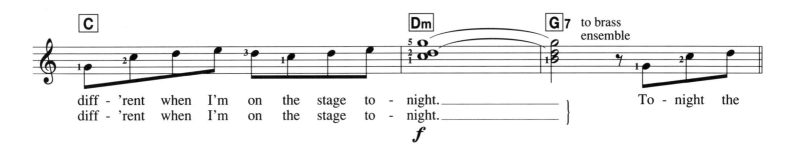

diff - 'rent when I'm on the stage to - night._____ To - night the
diff - 'rent when I'm on the stage to - night._____
f

CHORUS

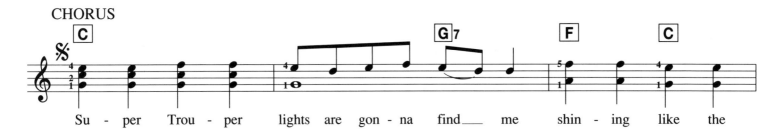

Su - per Trou - per lights are gon - na find___ me shin - ing like the

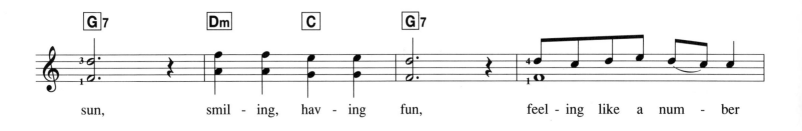

sun, smil - ing, hav - ing fun, feel - ing like a num - ber

16

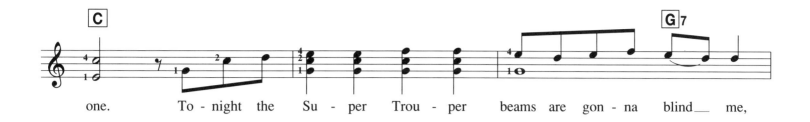

one. To - night the Su - per Trou - per beams are gon - na blind___ me,

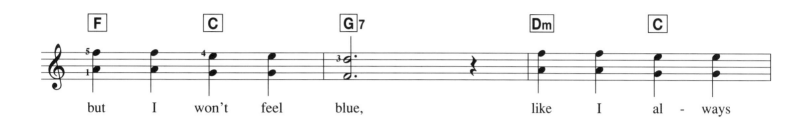

but I won't feel blue, like I al - ways

do, 'cause some - where in the crowd___ there's you.___

INTERLUDE

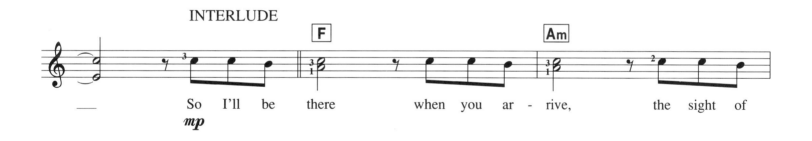

___ So I'll be there when you ar - rive, the sight of
mp

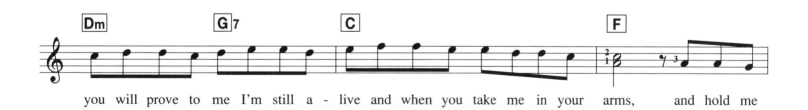

you will prove to me I'm still a - live and when you take me in your arms, and hold me

tight, I know it's gon - na mean so much to - night.___ To - night the
cresc. *f*

GIMME! GIMME! GIMME! (A MAN AFTER MIDNIGHT)

Words & Music by Benny Andersson & Björn Ulvaeus

Suggested registration: clarinet
Rhythm: rock
Tempo: medium (♩ = 116)

VERSE

1. Half past twelve and I'm watch-in' the late show in my flat all a-lone, how I

hate to spend the eve-ning on my own. Au-tumn winds blow-in' out-side my win-dow, as I

look a-round the room, and it makes me so de-pressed to see the gloom. add guitar

BRIDGE

There's not a soul out there. No - one to hear my

prayer. cresc.

CHORUS

Dm / Gm / C / Dm / Gm / Dm

Gim - me! Gim - me! Gim - me! A man___ af - ter mid - night, won't some - bo - dy help me chase the

f

C / Dm / Gm / C / Dm

sha - dows a - way?___ Gim - me! Gim - me! Gim - me! A man___ af - ter mid - night,

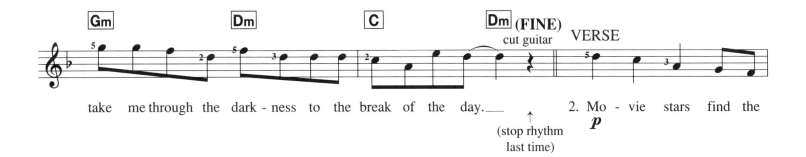

Gm / Dm / C / Dm **(FINE)** cut guitar VERSE

take me through the dark - ness to the break of the day.___ 2. Mo - vie stars find the

(stop rhythm last time) *p*

G

end of the rain - bow, with a for - tune to win, it's so dif - f'rent from the world I'm li - vin'

Dm / G

in. Tired of T. V., I o - pen the win - dow, and I

D. 𝄋 *al Fine*
add guitar

Dm

gaze in - to the night, but there's no - thing there to see, no one in sight.

KNOWING ME, KNOWING YOU

Words & Music by Benny Andersson, Stig Anderson & Björn Ulvaeus

Suggested registration: flute
Rhythm: 8 beat
Tempo: medium (♩ = 120)

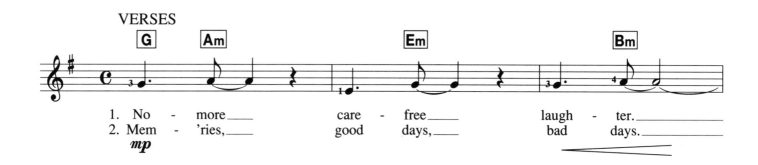

1. No - more____ care - free____ laugh - ter.____
2. Mem - 'ries,____ good days,____ bad days.____

mp

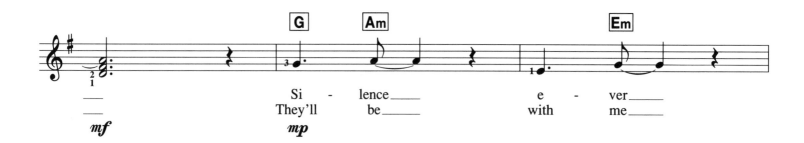

____ Si - lence____ e - ver
They'll be____ with me____

mf *mp*

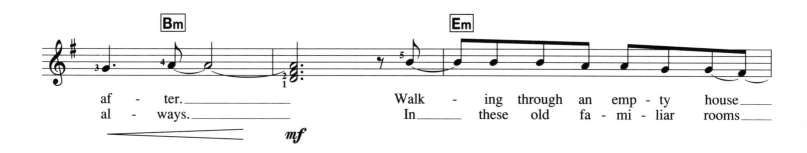

af - ter.____ Walk - ing through an emp - ty house____
al - ways.____ In these old fa - mi - liar rooms____

mf

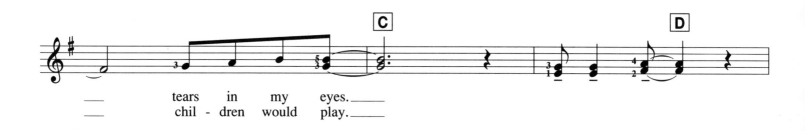

____ tears in my eyes.____
____ chil - dren would play.____

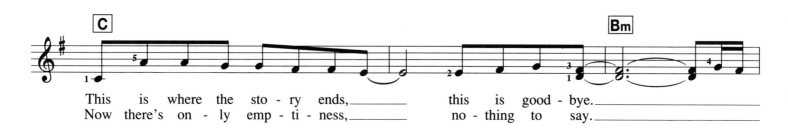

This is where the sto - ry ends,____ this is good - bye.____
Now there's on - ly emp - ti - ness,____ no - thing to say.____

CHORUS

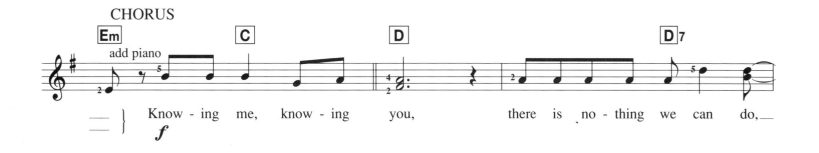

Know - ing me, know - ing you, there is no - thing we can do, _

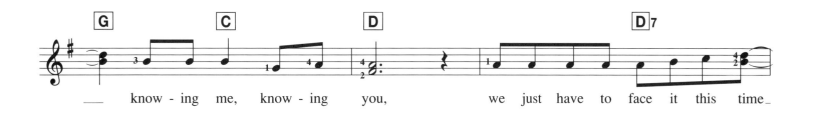

know - ing me, know - ing you, we just have to face it this time _

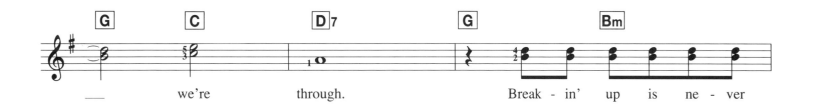

_ we're through. Break - in' up is ne - ver

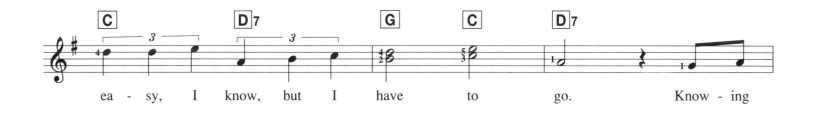

ea - sy, I know, but I have to go. Know - ing

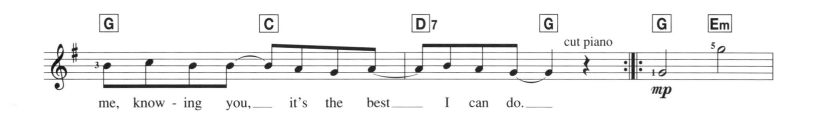

me, know - ing you, _ it's the best _ I can do. _

(Repeat and Fade)

MONEY, MONEY, MONEY

Words & Music by Benny Andersson & Björn Ulvaeus

Suggested registration: guitar
Rhythm: rock
Tempo: medium (♩ = 116)

1. I work all night, I work all day to
(2.) man like that is hard to find, but

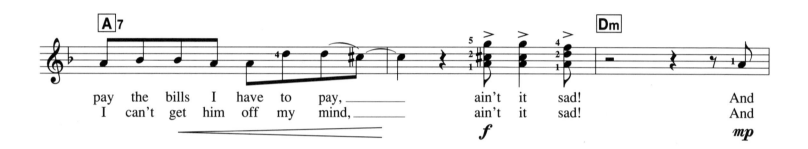

pay the bills I have to pay, _____ ain't it sad! And
I can't get him off my mind, _____ ain't it sad! And

still there ne-ver seems to be a sin-gle pen-ny left for me, _____ that's too bad!
if he hap-pens to be free I bet he would-n't fan-cy me, _____ that's too bad!

___ In my dreams I have a plan, _____
So I must leave, I'll have to go _____

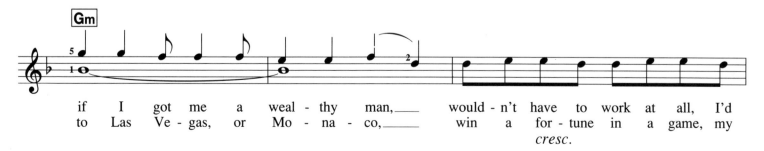

if I got me a weal-thy man, _____ would-n't have to work at all, I'd
to Las Ve-gas, or Mo-na-co, _____ win a for-tune in a game, my

cresc.

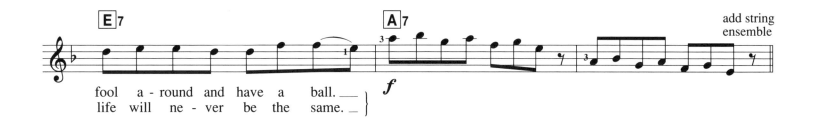

fool a - round and have a ball. ___
life will ne - ver be the same. __ }

CHORUS

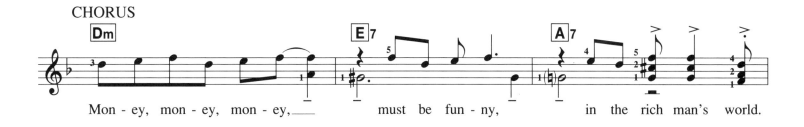

Mon - ey, mon - ey, mon - ey, ___ must be fun - ny, in the rich man's world.

Mon - ey, mon - ey, mon - ey, ___ al - ways sun - ny, ___

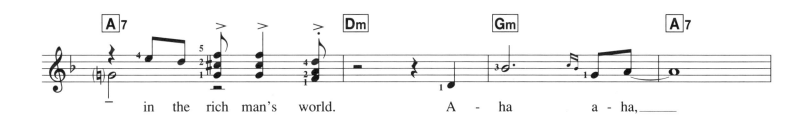

in the rich man's world. A - ha a - ha, ___

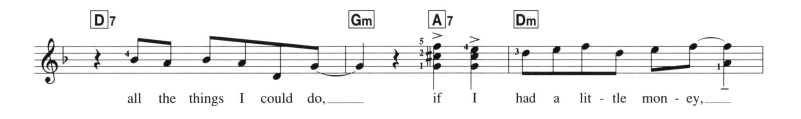

all the things I could do, ___ if I had a lit - tle mon - ey, ___

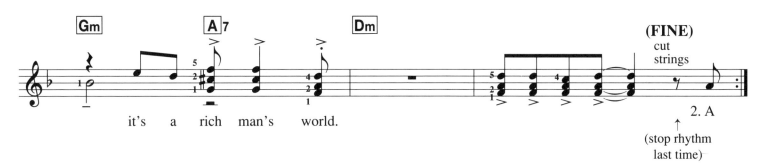

it's a rich man's world.

(FINE)
cut strings

2. A
(stop rhythm last time)

TAKE A CHANCE ON ME
Words & Music by Benny Andersson & Björn Ulvaeus

Suggested registration: trumpet
Rhythm: rock
Tempo: medium (♩ = 126)

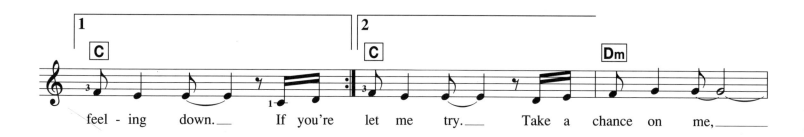

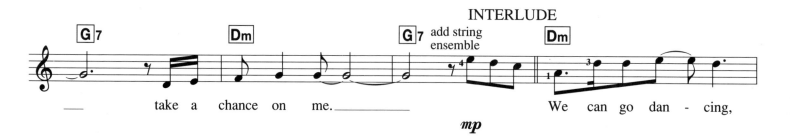

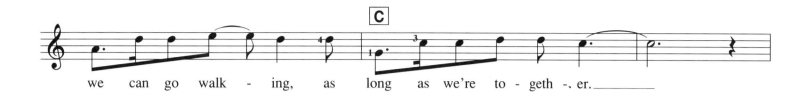

we can go walk - ing, as long as we're to - geth -, er._____

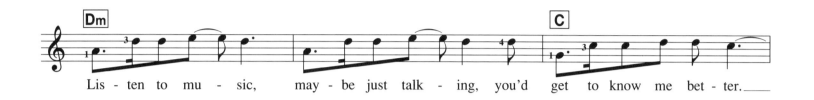

Lis - ten to mu - sic, may - be just talk - ing, you'd get to know me bet - ter.____

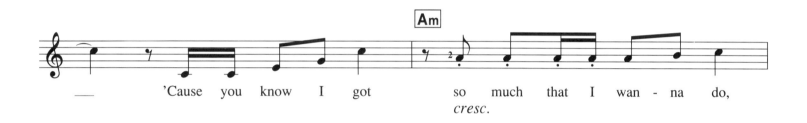

____ 'Cause you know I got so much that I wan - na do,

cresc.

when I dream I'm a - lone with you, it's ma - gic._____

f

You want me to leave it there, a - fraid of a love af - fair, but I

mp   *cresc.*

think you know _____ that I can't let go._____ If you

f   *mf*

(D.S. and fade)
cut strings

NINA, PRETTY BALLERINA

Words & Music by Benny Andersson & Björn Ulvaeus

Suggested registration: horn
Rhythm: rock
Tempo: quite fast (♩ = 152)

1. Ev - 'ry day in the morn - ing on her way to the of - fice you can
(2.) back ev - 'ry morn - ing to her work at the of - fice, and an -

see her as she catch - es a train. ___ Just a face a - mong a mil - lion fac -
oth - er week to live in a dream. ___ And an - oth - er row of ear - ly mor -

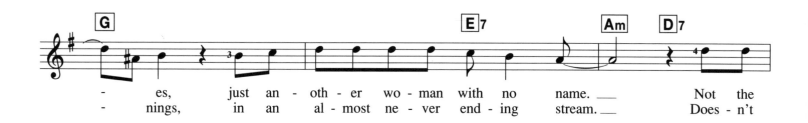

- es, just an - oth - er wo - man with no name. ___ Not the
- nings, in an al - most ne - ver end - ing stream. ___ Does - n't

girl you'd re - mem - ber, but she's still some - thing spe - cial, if you knew her I am sure you'd a - gree,
talk ve - ry of - ten, kind of shy and un - cer - tain, ev - 'ry - bo - dy seems to think she's a bore,

___ 'cause I know she's got a lit - tle se - cret, Fri - day
___ but they would - n't know her lit - tle se - cret, what her

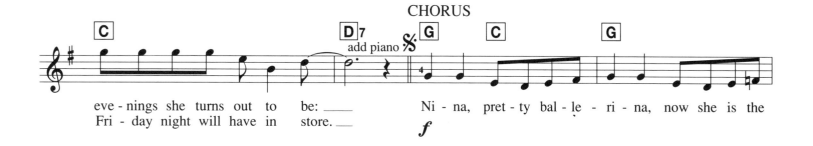

eve - nings she turns out to be: ___ Ni - na, pret - ty bal - le - ri - na, now she is the
Fri - day night will have in store. ___

queen of the danc - ing floor. ___ This is the mo - ment she's wait - ed for, ___

___ just like Cin - der - el - la ___ just like Cin - der - el - la. Ni - na, pret - ty bal - le -

ri - na, who would e - ver think she could be this way? ___ But she knows

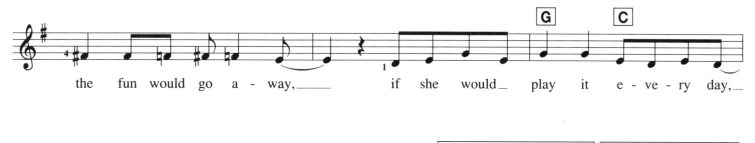

the fun would go a - way, ___ if she would ___ play it e - ve - ry day, ___

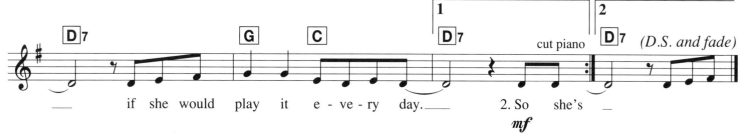

___ if she would play it e - ve - ry day. ___ 2. So she's ___

SUMMER NIGHT CITY

Words & Music by Benny Andersson & Björn Ulvaeus

Suggested registration: synth.
Rhythm: rock
Tempo: medium (♩ = 126)

CHORUS

Wait - ing for the sun - rise, soul___ danc - ing in the dark, sum - mer night ci - ty.___
mp

___ Walk - in' in the moon - light, love___ ma - kin' in a park,

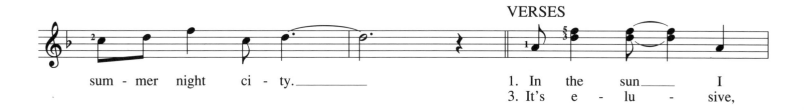

sum - mer night ci - ty.___

VERSES

1. In the sun___ I
3. It's e - lu - sive,

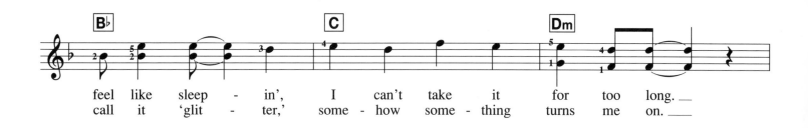

feel like sleep - in', I can't take it for too long.___
call it 'glit - ter,' some - how some - thing turns me on.___

My im - pa - tience slow - ly creep - in' up my spine and grow - in' strong.___
Some folks on - ly see the lit - ter, we don't miss 'em when they're gone.___

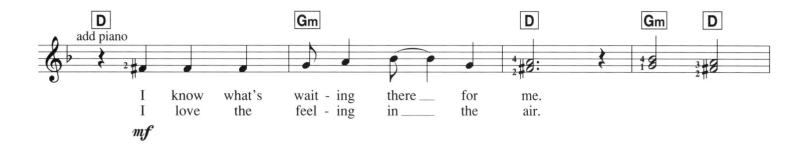

I know what's wait - ing there ___ for me.
I love the feel - ing in ___ the air.

mf

To - night I'm loose and fan - cy free. Ah, ___
My kind of peo - ple ev - 'ry - where. Ah, ___

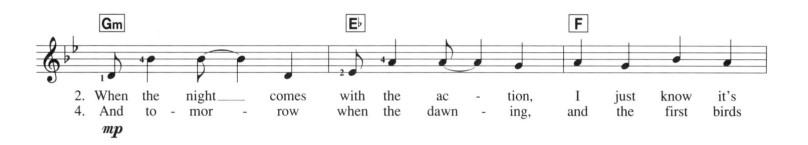

2. When the night ___ comes with the ac - tion, I just know it's
4. And to - mor - row when the dawn - ing, and the first birds

mp

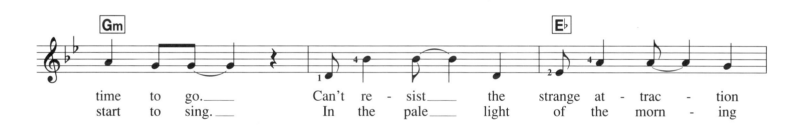

time to go. ___ Can't re - sist ___ the strange at - trac - tion
start to sing. ___ In the pale ___ light of the morn - ing

from that gi - ant dy - na - mo. ___ Lots to take and
no - thing's worth re - mem - ber - ing. ___ It's a dream, it's

D.C. (twice)
Fade on CHORUS *last time*

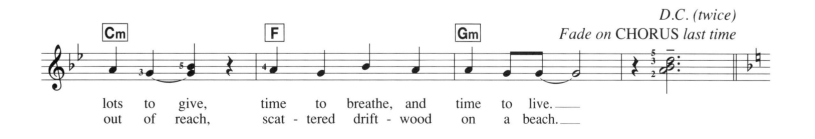

lots to give, time to breathe, and time to live. ___
out of reach, scat - tered drift - wood on a beach. ___

MAMMA MIA

Words & Music by Benny Andersson, Stig Anderson & Björn Ulvaeus

Suggested registration: trumpet
Rhythm: rock
Tempo: medium (♩ = 126)

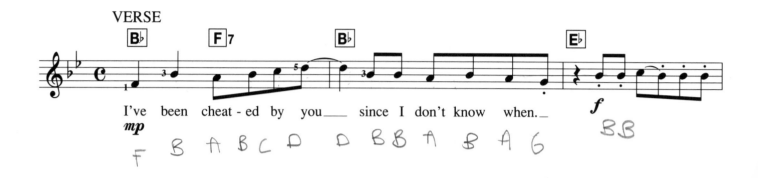

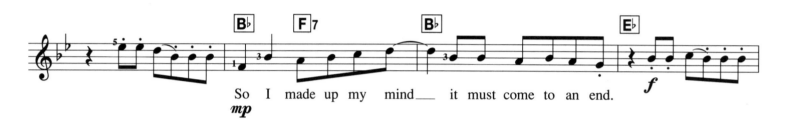

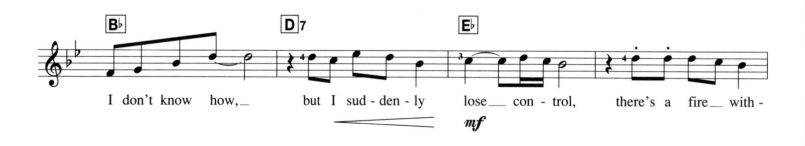

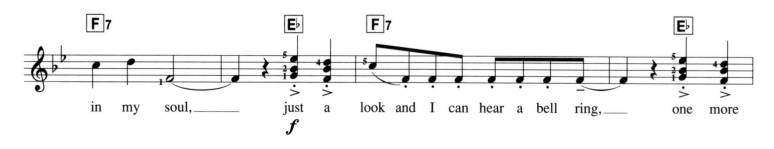

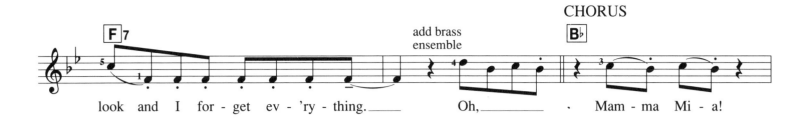

look and I for - get ev - 'ry - thing.____ Oh,_____ · Mam - ma Mi - a!

Here I go____ a - gain, my, my! How can I re - sist you?

Mam - ma Mi - a! Does it show____ a - gain, my, my!

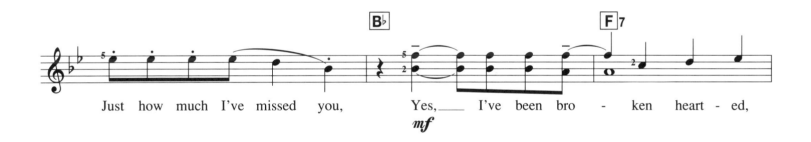

Just how much I've missed you, Yes,____ I've been bro - ken heart - ed,

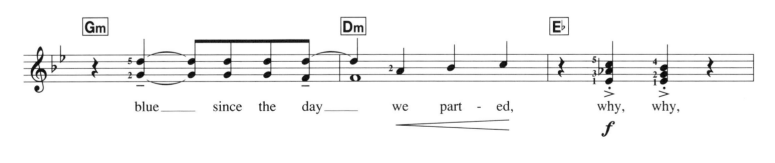

blue____ since the day____ we part - ed, why, why,

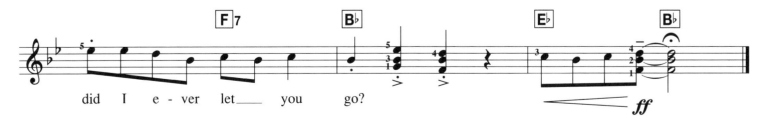

did I e - ver let____ you go?

WHY DID IT HAVE TO BE ME?

Words & Music by Benny Andersson & Björn Ulvaeus

Suggested registration: clarinet
Rhythm: swing
Tempo: medium (♩ = 116)

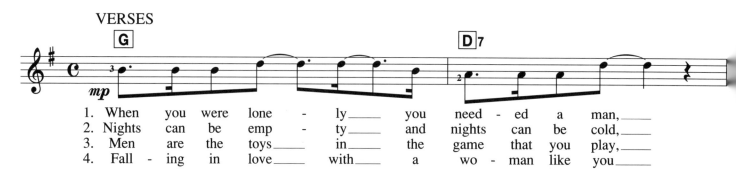

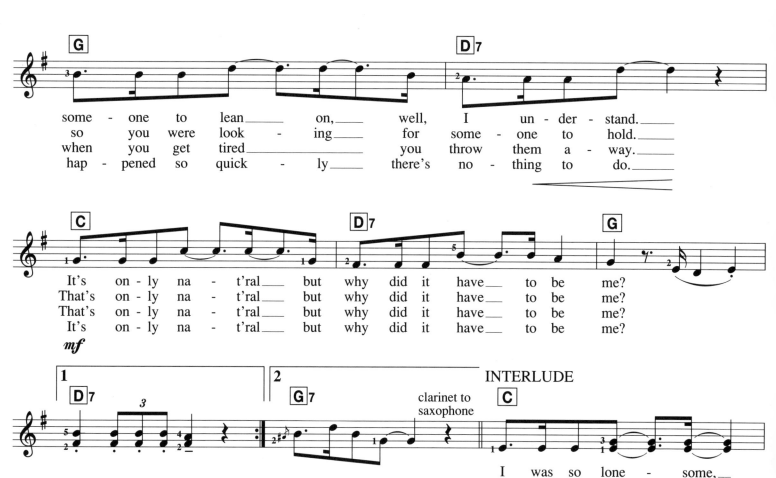

al - ways thought you knew the rea - son why.____

cresc.

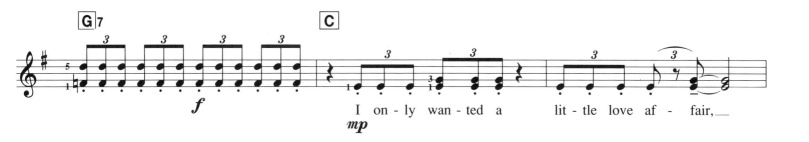

I on - ly wan - ted a lit - tle love af - fair,____

mp

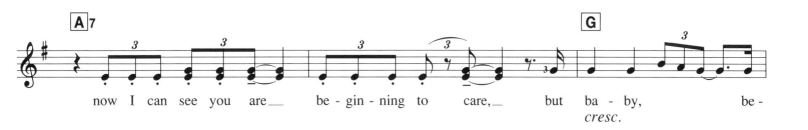

now I can see you are____ be - gin - ning to care,____ but ba - by, be -

cresc.

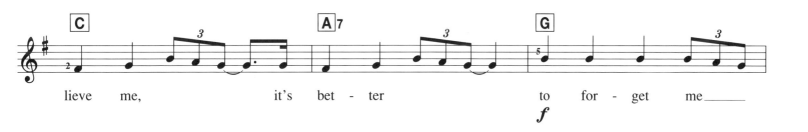

lieve me, it's bet - ter to for - get me____

f

INSTRUMENTAL

mf

D.C. first time (verses 3 and 4)
Repeat instrumental second time, and fade

saxophone to clarinet

f

DANCING QUEEN

Words & Music by Benny Andersson, Stig Anderson & Björn Ulvaeus

Suggested registration: piano
Rhythm: disco
Tempo: medium (♩ = 100)

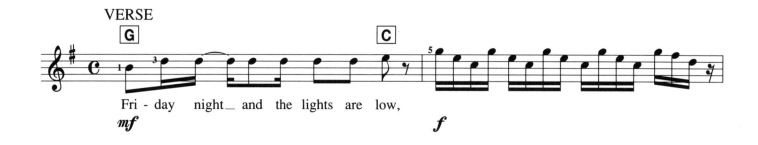

Fri - day night__ and the lights are low,

look - ing out__ for a place to go.___ Oh,___ where they play__ the right mu - sic,

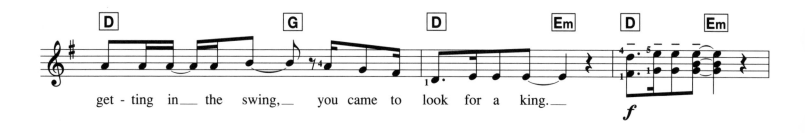

get - ting in__ the swing,__ you came to look for a king.___

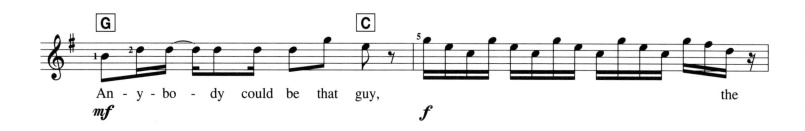

An - y - bo - dy could be that guy, the

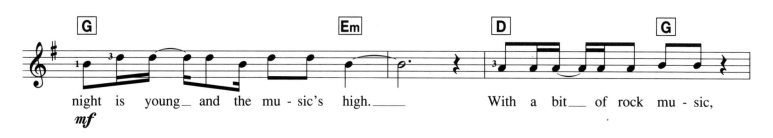

night is young__ and the mu - sic's high.___ With a bit__ of rock mu - sic,

ev - 'ry - thing__ is fine,__ you're in the mood for a dance,__ and when you

CHORUS

get the chance.__ You are the dan - cing queen,__ young and sweet,__ on - ly

se - ven - teen.__ Dan - cing queen,__ feel the beat__ from the

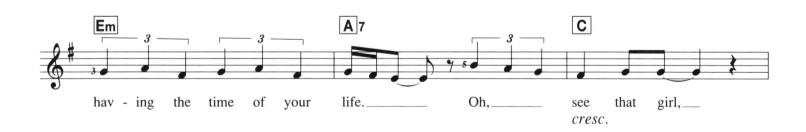

tam - bour - ine.__ You can dance,__ you can jive,____

hav - ing the time of your life._____ Oh,_____ see that girl,__

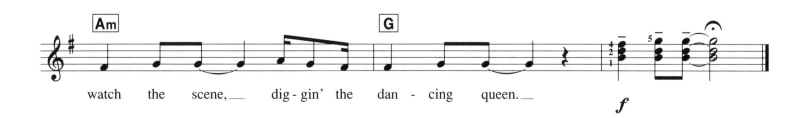

watch the scene,__ dig - gin' the dan - cing queen.__

35

THANK YOU FOR THE MUSIC

Words & Music by Benny Andersson & Björn Ulvaeus

Suggested registration: oboe
Rhythm: rock
Tempo: medium (♩ = 104)

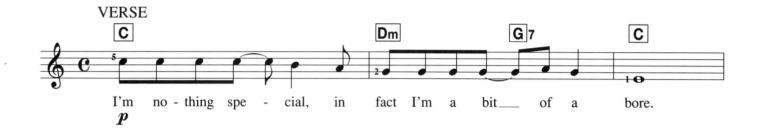

I'm no-thing spe-cial, in fact I'm a bit___ of a bore.

If I tell a joke___ you've pro-bab-ly heard___ it be -

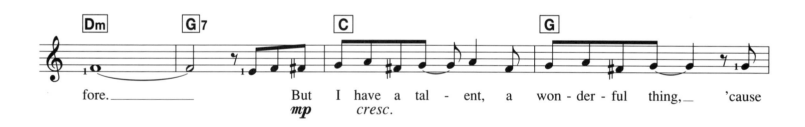

fore._____ But I have a tal - ent, a won-der-ful thing,___ 'cause

ev - 'ry-one lis - tens when I start to sing,___ I'm so grate-ful and proud,___

___ all I want___ is to sing___ it out loud. So I say

CHORUS

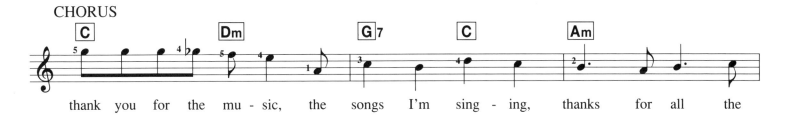

thank you for the mu - sic, the songs I'm sing - ing, thanks for all the

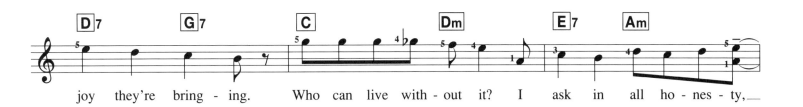

joy they're bring - ing. Who can live with - out it? I ask in all ho - nes - ty,

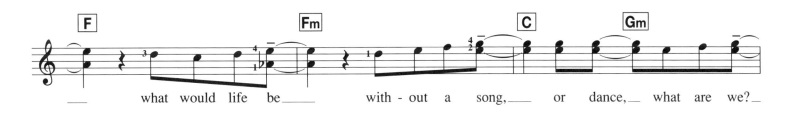

what would life be with - out a song, or dance, what are we?

So I say thank you for the mu - sic, for giv - ing it to me.

INTERLUDE

brass to oboe

mp

I've been so

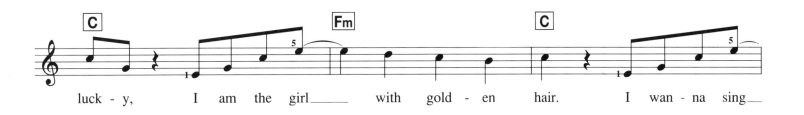

luck - y, I am the girl with gold - en hair. I wan - na sing

it out to ev - 'ry - bo - dy, what a joy, what a life,
cresc.

CHORUS

what a chance.___ Thank you for the mu - sic, the songs I'm sing - ing,
f

thanks for all the joy they're bring - ing, who can live with - out it? I

ask in all ho - nes - ty,___ what would life be___ with - out a song___

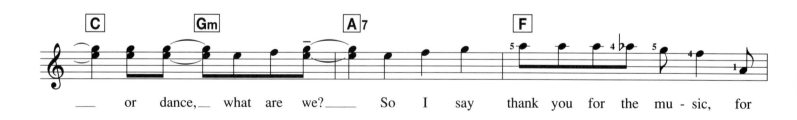

___ or dance,___ what are we?___ So I say thank you for the mu - sic, for

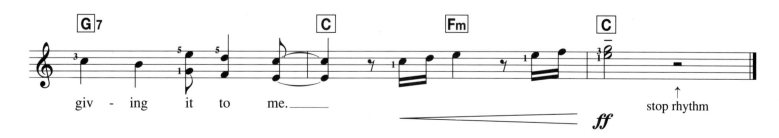

giv - ing it to me.___
stop rhythm
ff

MASTER CHORD CHART

C
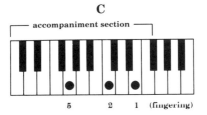

Cm
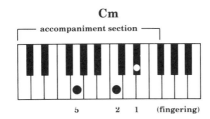

C7
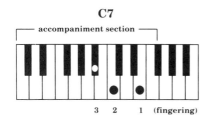

D♭
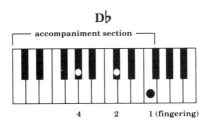

C♯m
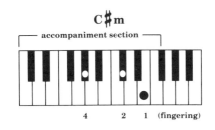

D♭(C♯)7
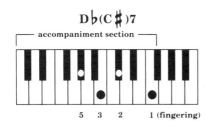

D
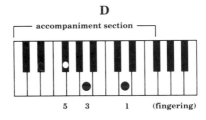

Dm
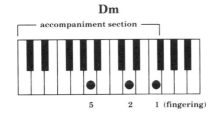

D7
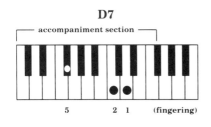

E♭
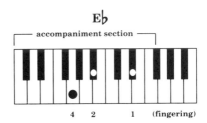

E♭m
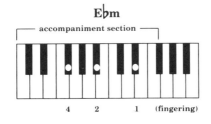

E♭7
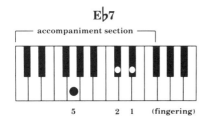

E
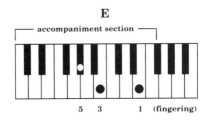

Em
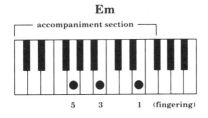

E7
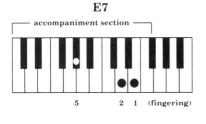

F
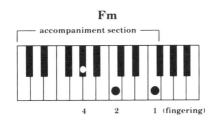

Fm
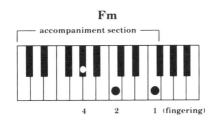

F7
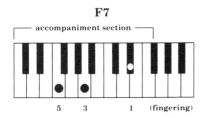

MASTER CHORD CHART

G♭(F♯)

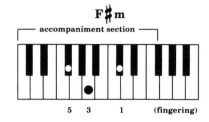

F♯m

G♭(F♯)7

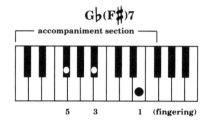

G

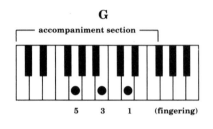

Gm

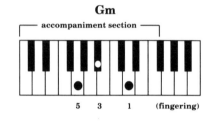

G7

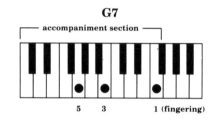

A♭

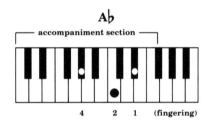

A♭m

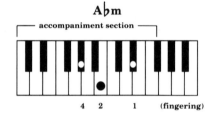

A♭7

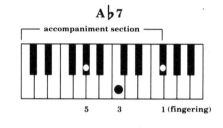

A

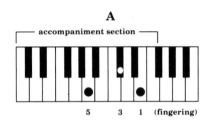

Am

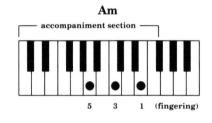

A7

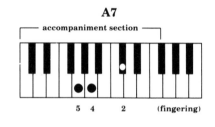

B♭

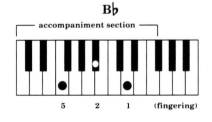

B♭m

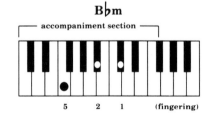

B♭7

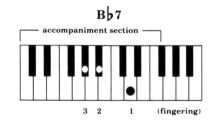

B

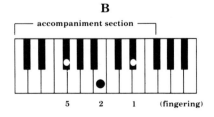

Bm

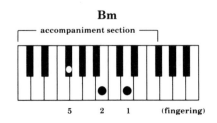

B7

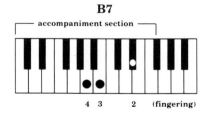

Printed by Printwise (Haverhill) Limited, Suffolk   1/09 (168543)